Developing Literacy
SPEAKING & LISTENING

PHOTOCOPIABLE ACTIVITIES
FOR THE LITERACY HOUR

year
1

Christine Moorcroft
and Ray Barker

A & C BLACK

Contents

Published 2006 by A & C Black Publishers Limited
38 Soho Square, London W1D 3HB
www.acblack.com

ISBN-10: 0-7136-7369-9
ISBN-13: 978-0-7136-7369-2

Copyright text © Christine Moorcroft, 2006
Copyright illustrations © Susan Hutchison and Sue Woollatt, 2006
Copyright cover illustration © Andy Robb, 2006
Editors: Lynne Williamson and Marie Lister
Designer: Heather Billin

The authors and publishers would like to thank Fleur Lawrence and Kim Perez for their advice in producing this series of books.

A CIP catalogue record for this book is available from the British Library.

Printed and bound in Great Britain by Cromwell Press Ltd, Trowbridge, Wiltshire.

A & C Black uses paper produced with elemental chlorine-free pulp, harvested from managed sustainable forests.

Introduction

Developing Literacy: Speaking and Listening is a series of seven photocopiable activity books for the Literacy Hour. Each book provides a range of speaking and listening activities and supports the teaching and learning objectives identified in *Curriculum Guidance for the Foundation Stage* and by the Primary National Strategy in *Speaking, Listening, Learning: working with children in Key Stages 1 and 2*.

Speaking and listening skills are vital to children's intellectual and social development, particularly in helping them to:

- develop creativity;
- interact with others;
- solve problems;
- speculate and discourse;
- form social relationships;
- build self-confidence.

The activities in this book focus on the following four aspects of speaking and listening:

- **Speaking:** being able to speak clearly; developing and sustaining ideas in talk
- **Listening:** developing active listening strategies; using skills of analysis
- **Group discussion and interaction:** taking different roles in groups; working collaboratively; making a range of contributions
- **Drama:** improvisation; working in role; scripting and performing; responding to performances

Using the activity sheets

The materials show how speaking and listening can be relevant to all parts of literacy lessons, in whole-class work, in group or paired work, during independent work and in plenary sessions. The activities encourage the inclusion of all learners, since talking and contributing to group work are often more accessible than writing for lower-achieving children and for those who speak English as an additional language.

Extension activities

Most of the activity sheets end with a challenge (**Now try this!**), which reinforces and extends the children's learning and provides the teacher with an opportunity for assessment. These more challenging activities might be appropriate for only a few children; it is not expected that the whole class should complete them. For some of the extension activities, the children will need a notebook or a separate sheet of paper.

Organisation

Few resources are needed besides scissors, glue, word banks and simple dictionaries. Access to ICT resources – computers, video, tape recorders – will also be useful at times.
To help teachers select appropriate learning experiences for their pupils, the activities are grouped into sections within the book. The pages need not be presented in the order in which they appear, unless stated otherwise.
The sheets are intended to support, rather than direct the teacher's planning.

Brief notes are provided at the bottom of each page, giving ideas and suggestions for making the most of the activity sheet. They may include suggestions for a whole-class introduction, a plenary session or follow-up work. These notes may be masked before photocopying if desired. More detailed notes and suggestions can be found on pages 6–8.

Effective group work

Many of the activities involve children working in groups. Here are some ideas to consider as you prepare for group work.

Before you start

HOW?

- How are deadlines and groupings made clear to groups?
- How might different children undertake different tasks?
- How will you organise time and space to give children the opportunity to rehearse and practise new skills?
- How will the children reflect on what they have learned about talk and its impact?

WHEN?

- When is working in a group appropriate?
- When is speaking and listening the focus of an activity?
- When is speaking and listening the outcome?
- When is it right for one child to become 'an expert' and inform others?

WHERE?

- Where in the class is the work going to take place in order to give space and manage noise levels?
- Where is it best for you to be to monitor the groups?
- Where might group work result in a finished product, such as a leaflet, and what resources will you need?

Tips for grouping children

- Be clear about the nature and purpose of the task.
- Decide which type of grouping is best for your purpose (pairs, attainment groups, friendship groups).
- Consider the advantages of mixed- or single-sex groupings in your particular class.
- Consider how you will include all abilities in these groups.
- Think carefully about who will lead groups and how you can vary this.
- Aim to vary the experience for the children: for example, using different groupings, ways of recording or learning environments. Experiment with what works best for different kinds of learners.

Your role

The notes in this book suggest an active role for you as a teacher, and give examples of how you can develop children's learning. Your role will vary from activity to activity, but here are some general points to bear in mind when working with children on speaking and listening activities:

- Be challenging in your choice of topics.
- Don't be afraid to use the correct language for talk: for example, *dialogue, gesture, narrator, negotiate, open and closed questions* and so on.
- Set the ground rules: everyone has a right to speak but everyone also has a duty to listen to others, take turns and so on.
- Move around to monitor what is happening in the groups. You can move on group discussions by developing and questioning what the children say.
- Provide models of the patterns of language expected for particular kinds of speech.
- Try to steer children away from using closed questions.
- Ensure children give extended answers and always ask them to explain their thinking.
- Allow children time to formulate their responses and treat everyone's responses with respect – but avoid praising every answer.

Assessment

An assessment sheet is provided on page 48 for children to assess their own progress. The children can complete the sheet on their own or in discussion with you. It is not expected that you will be able to assess the entire class at any one time. It is best to focus on a small group of children each week, although whole-class monitoring may be possible with certain activities, such as drama activities where children perform to the class.

Other activities in the book are ideal for the collection of evidence over the year (for example, *My Saturday, Story characters, Story tape, Story video, Favourite story setting*) and for children to assess one another's skills in speaking and listening (*Puss in Boots: 2, Pattern cards, Pirate treasure, Make a minibeast, Racer: 1*). All the information should be assimilated for an end-of-year summary to facilitate target setting and the transition to Year 2.

Notes on the activities

Speaking

The activities in this section provide contexts to encourage the children to speak clearly, audibly and with control to a partner, another adult, their group or the class and to be aware of their audience.

At the funfair (page 9). You could link this activity with design and technology, using construction material with cogs to make fairground rides. **Vocabulary**: big wheel, candy floss, carousel, fair, Ferris wheel, funfair, helter-skelter, ride, roundabout, sideshow, stall, story, talk.

My Saturday (page 10). Use this activity on a Monday, when the children might remember what they did on Saturday. You could give them the sheet on the previous Friday and ask them to draw the pictures for homework. Link this with maths work on time, and science work on day and night. The extension activity develops skills in asking and answering questions. **Vocabulary**: afternoon, day, evening, label, morning, night, Saturday, tell, time, yesterday.

At the supermarket (page 11). The children could talk about their own experiences of going to the supermarket, and what they like/dislike. Link this with work in numeracy (money and shopping). **Vocabulary**: car, car park, setting, shop, shopping, story, supermarket, talk, tell, trolley.

Storyteller (page 12). Here, the children retell a well-known story of their choice. Alternatively, you could ask them to describe the scene and to predict what will happen next. The activity offers an ICT opportunity to use software which provides word lists, such as *Clicker* (Crick Software, www.cricksoft.com), to support the children's storytelling. **Vocabulary**: after that, next, story, tell, then.

There was an old woman… (page 13). Once the children have told the story, they could glue the pictures onto a sheet of paper. Lower-achieving children could then write labels for the animals; higher-achieving children could write sentences. Encourage them to read aloud what they have written. The activity can be linked with science (the foods which animals eat). As an extension, the children could draw and cut out pictures for another song or rhyme they know, for a partner to put in order. **Vocabulary**: bird, cat, cow, dog, fly, horse, old woman, spider, story, swallow, tell.

Puss in Boots: 1 and 2 (pages 14–15). The children could tell the story to a partner and then retell it to younger children. You could provide draw-string bags and toy rabbits and birds for use as props. **Vocabulary**: bag, boots, coach, ogre, partridge, Puss, rabbit, read, story, tell.

Story cards (page 16). Discuss how the children know which story the card shows. As an extension, the children could make a different story card, and tell the story to a friend. **Vocabulary**: ball, bricks, coach, fairy godmother, grandma, house, little, midnight, path, pig, rags, sticks, story, straw, tell, twelve o'clock, ugly sisters, wolf, woods.

The Gingerbread Man (page 17). Ask the children about the times when they speak quietly, and why. When do they speak loudly, and why? If possible, provide tape recorders for the children to record their reading of the passage. Play back the recordings and invite others to comment. **Vocabulary**: cook, fast, gingerbread, little old woman, loud, loudly, oven, quiet, quietly, story, tell.

Say the words (page 18). The children could first talk to a partner about what is happening in the pictures. Draw out that when people say something to someone else they usually expect an answer. The activity offers an ICT opportunity to use software with word lists to support storytelling. **Vocabulary**: answer, character, conversation, listen, say, scene, speak, speech bubble, story.

Listening

These activities develop children's skills as active listeners and help them to join in meaningful discussions. Demonstrate good listening by enlisting the help of another adult for a short role-play of bad listening (fidgeting, looking away from the speaker, interrupting, daydreaming and so on). Ask what is wrong and what the listener *should* do.

Story characters (page 19). Here, the children focus on listening to details in a story: names of characters; whether they are human or animals; whether they are good or bad (and why); what they like and dislike. Discuss examples of words that can be used to describe characters. You could link this with sentence-level work (writing names with an initial capital) and text-level work on character profiles. **Vocabulary**: animal, bad, character, describe, good, human, listen, name, story, tell.

The Big Pancake (page 20). To make the activity easier, tell the story while the children follow it on the story map and then ask them to fill in the gaps. For higher-achieving children, you could mask some more of the words (such as 'man' and 'cat') before photocopying the sheet. **Vocabulary**: along, door, field, gate, label, on, pancake, path, rolled, through, wall.

Spike the hungry hedgehog (page 21). This activity has connections with word-level work (reading the days of the week and developing vocabulary in connection with topics in other subjects), and also with sentence-level work on plurals. It can be used in conjunction with work on ourselves in science (the needs of all animals for food). **Vocabulary**: ants, ate, beetles, eat, food, Friday, hedgehog, hungry, Monday, Saturday, slug, spiders, Thursday, Tuesday, Wednesday, worms.

The sunflower (page 22). Remind the child doing the speaking to look carefully at the pictures and to speak clearly. Tell the other child to listen carefully and to match what he or she is told to one of the pictures. Some children might be able to work in groups of three with one acting as evaluator. The activity links with sentence-level work (connective words and phrases) and science (life cycles). For the extension activity, the children will need to find out about life cycles using information books. **Vocabulary:** bud, flower, grow, label, leaf, leaves, life cycle, light, plant, roots, seed, shoot, soil, stem, sun, tell, warmth, water.

Pattern cards (page 23). Ask the children to name each shape and to say whether it is at the top, bottom or in the middle of the pattern. Also ask them to think about whether the shape is small or large, and to use these words in their descriptions. The activity can be used in maths lessons on shape and space. **Vocabulary:** big, bottom, circle, large, long, middle, oblong, pattern, rectangle, shape, short, small, square, tell, top, triangle.

Pirate treasure (page 24). The children could first take turns to give directions from one part of the classroom to another. Link this with mapping work in geography lessons. ICT can be introduced by asking the children to direct a programmable toy along a simple route chalked on the floor. **Vocabulary:** along, left, right, route, stop, straight on, tell, treasure, turn.

Make a minibeast (page 25). First show the children photographs of a snail and a spider; name the body parts and describe their shapes. Demonstrate the actions involved in making the models, and ask the children for words for these actions and for the shapes. Link this with science lessons on living things. **Vocabulary:** body, coil, feelers, head, legs, long, roll, shell, snail, spider, spiral.

Story tape (page 26). During the plenary, discuss what the children enjoyed about the recording. Did they prefer the recording or the book? Why? (They might prefer the book because it lets them imagine the atmosphere of the setting and the voices of the characters.) Groups could listen to and comment on recordings produced by other children. **Vocabulary:** author, book, character, cover, listen, music, narrator, sound, story tape/CD, title, voice.

Information video (page 27). It is useful for the children to compare finding information from books and from videos. Draw out that a video can show real-life objects, animals or places and can also show what they sound like; it can explain things by talking about them while using pictures and diagrams to help; it can add atmosphere through the use of music. Help the children to distinguish between this type of video/DVD and a story video. **Vocabulary:** cartoon, diagram, facts, fiction, information, music, non-fiction, real life, talk, video/DVD.

Story video (page 28). Encourage the children to talk about how the story has been presented. If they have read the book it is based on, ask whether the characters look how they expected. Does this spoil or add to their enjoyment of the story? **Vocabulary:** character, cover, fiction, information, music, narrator, non-fiction, story, talk, title, video/DVD.

Group discussion and interaction

In this section the children use talk to explore and share ideas, and they collaborate in shared activities, such as solving a problem and take different roles in groups: for example, suggesting ideas, acting as scribe, asking questions for information or clarification.

Rhyme characters (page 29). In this activity the children deduce the identity of a nursery rhyme character by asking questions. The questions could be framed so that they can be answered only by 'Yes' or 'No', or you could allow open questions. **Vocabulary:** answer, character, nursery rhyme, question, talk, who.

Animal partners (page 30). Model some questions before the children begin: for example, 'Do you have fur?' 'Do you have sharp claws?' 'Do you meow?' Alternatively, display the animals on an interactive whiteboard and choose one. Encourage the children to deduce which it is by asking questions which can be answered by 'Yes' or 'No'. After each question has been answered, ask the children which of the pictures should be crossed off. **Vocabulary:** animal, answer, beak, cat, chimpanzee, claws, crab, duck, eat, feathers, feet, fins, fur, goldfish, grass, ladybird, legs, lizard, owl, question, scales, sheep, shell, snail, spider, spots, swim, tail, water, web, webbed, which, whiskers, wings, wool, worm.

Racer: 1 and 2 (pages 31–32). First discuss what happens in a car race and introduce the related vocabulary. The children will need to decide on their own rules, such as using a dice or spinner to determine how many spaces to move. This activity can be linked with work in citizenship on what is fair/unfair. **Vocabulary:** counter, crash, dice, fair, fast track, finish, instructions, overtake, pit stop, race, rule, skid, spin, spinner, start, take turns, unfair.

Giving presents (page 33). Remind the children of the rules for speaking and listening. Model how to encourage others to speak, by asking questions such as: 'Is that the kind of present you would choose for your mum?' 'How do you think this mum might be different from yours?' 'What makes you think she will like it?' Link this with citizenship work on making choices, including taking a vote. Discuss any stereotyping, such as choosing a football for a man or boy. Might a girl like a football? **Vocabulary:** answer, ask, choose, discuss, give, listen, present, question, talk, vote.

All kinds of books (page 34). Draw out that there are no 'right answers' – we like books for different reasons. The activity can be linked with text-level work on the features of books and with work in citizenship on making choices. **Vocabulary:** choice, choose, discuss, dislike, favourite, information, like, reason, rhyme, vote, why.

Favourite story setting (page 35). Stress that everyone should have a chance to speak and that the others should listen carefully. **Vocabulary**: choose, discuss, favourite, graph, listen, opinion, setting, story, tell, view, vote.

Our classroom (page 36). Allow opportunities for the groups to present their views to the class. This could be linked with work in citizenship, where the children's ideas lead to changes being made in the classroom. **Vocabulary**: choose, dislike, idea, like, listen, notes, opinion, talk, view.

Solve the problem (page 37). Draw out that everyone's view is valuable and that sometimes people may change their views. Allow opportunities for the groups to present their ideas to the class, and ask the children whether they changed their minds after listening to others. This could be linked with work in geography and in citizenship on improving the school grounds. **Vocabulary**: choose, idea, listen, opinion, problem, solution, solve, talk, tell, view.

Drama

These activities provide support for the children to use their voices, facial expressions and body movements to portray characters and to enact stories. The children are also encouraged to talk about the way in which a performance is enacted, saying what they enjoyed.

Wolf mask and **Goat mask** (pages 38 and 39). The children should first have read or listened to a story in which either or both characters appear: for example, *The Wolf and the Seven Little Kids*, *The Three Little Pigs*, *Little Red Riding Hood*, *The Three Billy Goats Gruff* or *What's the Time, Mr Wolf?* To cut out the eye holes in the masks, fold them into semi-circles before cutting. A mask helps children to enact the role of a character by providing a barrier between them and the audience. The masks can be used in hot-seating activities: a volunteer is seated on a chair (the 'hot seat'), wearing the mask. The others ask questions and the volunteer replies in role. Model some questions: for example (for a wolf), 'What do you eat?' 'How did you get into Grandma's house?' **Vocabulary**: act, ask, character, hot seat, mask, question, role, story.

A magic story (page 40). Ensure that the children are familiar with stories in which magic happens, and can distinguish magic from real life. When the children enact their stories they are likely to recreate stories they have read; encourage them to develop their own ideas from these. **Vocabulary**: act, bad, broom, character, evil, good, magic, magic spell, real, story, voice, wand.

My story character (page 41). Here, the children use a prop to explore a stock story character of their own invention (king, queen, prince or princess). Alternatively, the crown can be used to help them enact the role of a specific character in a traditional or modern story or rhyme. Allow the children time to 'play' with the character and explore what he or she might do, where and with

whom. The children could develop their ideas into a story to perform to the class. **Vocabulary**: act, character, crown, king, prince, princess, prop, queen, role, story.

Cinderella (page 42). Begin by inviting volunteers to retell parts of the story of *Cinderella*. Ask questions such as 'Which characters were doing wrong?' 'What were they doing wrong?' 'How could Cinderella have got help to stop their bullying?' 'Who could have helped her?' Link this with work in citizenship on what is right/wrong and fair/unfair, and on understanding the nature and effects of bullying. **Vocabulary**: act, bad, bully, character, good, role, scene, story, voice.

Goldilocks in the hot seat (page 43). The hot-seating activity can be carried out in groups or as a class. This links with sentence-level work on asking and answering questions. **Vocabulary**: answer, ask, character, hot seat, imagine, question, role, role-play, voice.

The Sleeping Beauty (page 44). Once the children have prepared their 'good wish', you could set up a cradle containing a doll dressed as a baby princess; working in groups, the children come out and make their wish. Link this with work in citizenship on friendship, right and wrong, and personal qualities which are useful for different people (such as a good friend or a leader). **Vocabulary**: act, baby, bad, baptism, christening, evil, fairy, good, imagine, king, magic spell, princess, queen, scene, voice, wish.

Who's talking? (page 45). Discuss how this picture story is different from narrative text (in which the characters' words are introduced or followed by phrases such as 'the man said'). This prepares the children for later work in which they read and write playscripts (omitting 'said', 'called', 'asked' and so on). Discuss with the children what makes a good performance, such as use of voice, gestures and movement. **Vocabulary**: asked, called, record, role, said, story, take turns, voice.

The Emperor's New Clothes (page 46). The children could mime the scene more than once, swapping roles, with one observing. Ask what the observer liked about the performance. Read the rest of the story to the children after they have completed the activity. There are opportunities to draw out citizenship issues such as right/wrong and fairness/unfairness. **Vocabulary**: character, emperor, lie, mime, pretend, scene, trick, true, untrue.

Jack and the Beanstalk (page 47). First let the children practise acting and speaking as if they were Jack exchanging the cow for some beans, his mother telling him off, and so on. Ask observers to notice how they showed feelings with their faces, body movements and voices. **Vocabulary**: act, action, character, expression, feeling, movement, voice.

How did you do? (page 48). This is a simple self-assessment sheet. It is not intended for use after every activity, but should be given when it is felt appropriate. Sections not applicable to the activity can be masked.

At the funfair

- ## What is happening in the picture?

Talk to a friend.

- ## What if you could step into the picture?

Make up a story.

Work with a friend.

Teachers' note First ask the children about the setting of this picture and introduce new vocabulary. Have the children been to a funfair? What did they do there? What did they see, hear and smell there? The children should work in pairs, taking turns to say something about the picture. Once they have described the scene in general, encourage them to look at the details.

**Developing Literacy
Speaking & Listening
Year 1
© A & C BLACK**

My Saturday

What did you do on Saturday **?**

• **Draw pictures. Label them.**

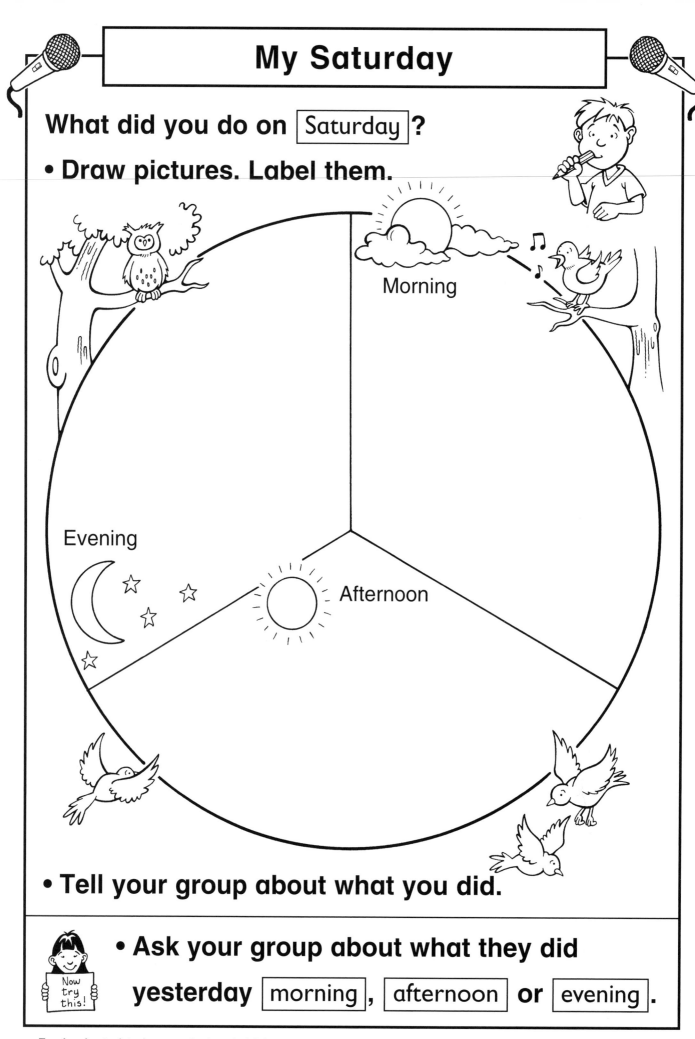

Morning

Evening

Afternoon

• **Tell your group about what you did.**

• **Ask your group about what they did**

yesterday morning **,** afternoon **or** evening **.**

Teachers' note Introduce or revise 'morning', 'afternoon' and 'evening'. Ask the children to draw and label small pictures showing what they did during each part of the day. Then encourage them to use their drawings as prompts when they tell the rest of the group about their day.

**Developing Literacy
Speaking & Listening
Year 1
© A & C BLACK**

At the supermarket

- **Cut out the pictures.**
- **Put them in order.**
- **Tell the story.**

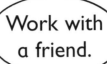

Work with a friend.

- **Talk about what else happened.**
- **Together, tell your group.**

Teachers' note Ask the children where this story takes place, and how they can tell. You could introduce the word 'setting'. Emphasise that the children will need to think about the order in which the mother and son do things. They could make up names for the characters. In the extension activity, encourage the children to use their own experience of supermarkets to make up what happened.

Developing Literacy
Speaking & Listening
Year 1
© A & C BLACK

Storyteller

- **Choose a picture.**
- **Tell the story to a friend.**

Now try this!

- **Draw a picture from another story.**
- **Tell your friend what happened in the story.**

Teachers' note Ask the children to identify the stories the pictures come from. Encourage them to ask questions as their partner tells the story: for example, 'Why did he/she do that?' 'Who is he/she?' 'Why was he running away?' For alternative ways to use the sheet, see page 6.

Developing Literacy Speaking & Listening Year 1
© A & C BLACK

There was an old woman...

- **Cut out the pictures.**
- **Put them in order.**
- **Tell the story to a friend.**

Teachers' note Start by singing the song *There Was an Old Woman who Swallowed a Fly* with the children. Then encourage them to say or sing the words of the song as they arrange the pictures in the correct order. When telling the story to a partner, the children should use the pictures as prompts (they could take turns to contribute).

Developing Literacy
Speaking & Listening
Year 1
© A & C BLACK

There was once a boy who had no mother and no father. But he had a cat called Puss. "How will we manage?" said the boy.

"I can help you," said Puss. "First I need some boots and a bag." So the boy brought them for him.

Puss put a lettuce in his bag. Then he left the bag in a field and hid. A rabbit crept into the bag to eat the lettuce. Puss quickly tied up the bag. Then he put on his boots and went to see the king.

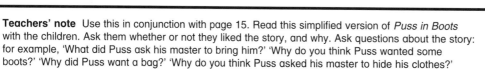

"This rabbit is a present from my master, the Marquis of Carabas," said Puss.

"I like rabbit," said the king.

The next day, Puss put some corn in his bag. Then he left the bag in the woods and hid. A partridge crept into the bag to eat the corn. Puss tied up the bag and went to see the king.

"This partridge is a present from my master, the Marquis of Carabas," said Puss.

"I like partridge," said the king.

The day after that, Puss saw a coach coming along the road. The king and his daughter, the princess, were in it. Puss told the boy to hide his clothes and jump into the river.

"Help!" called Puss. "The Marquis of Carabas is drowning!"

The king's men pulled the boy out of the water and gave him some very fine clothes to wear. The king asked the boy to get into the coach.

Puss ran to a castle. An ogre lived there. Puss said, "If you are a real ogre, you can turn yourself into anything you like."

"I can do that," said the ogre.

"Well," said Puss, "turn yourself into a mouse."

So the ogre turned himself into a little mouse. Puss ate him.

Soon the king's coach came along the road. "Welcome to the home of the Marquis of Carabas," said Puss. "Please stay for dinner."

The boy talked to the princess over dinner. She liked him. So the boy asked the king if he could marry her. The king smiled and said yes.

Teachers' note Use this in conjunction with page 15. Read this simplified version of *Puss in Boots* with the children. Ask them whether or not they liked the story, and why. Ask questions about the story: for example, 'What did Puss ask his master to bring him?' 'Why do you think Puss wanted some boots?' 'Why did Puss want a bag?' 'Why do you think Puss asked his master to hide his clothes?'

Developing Literacy
Speaking & Listening
Year 1
© A & C BLACK

Puss in Boots: 2

- **Cut out the cards.**
- **Tell the story to a friend.**

boots

partridge

coach

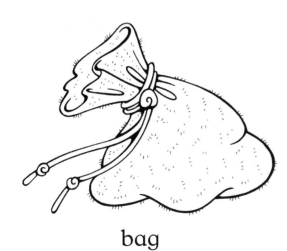

bag

rabbit

Teachers' note Photocopy this page onto card and use it in conjunction with page 14. The children should use the cards as props when they retell the story. They could colour the cards before cutting them out.

**Developing Literacy
Speaking & Listening
Year 1
© A & C BLACK**

Story cards

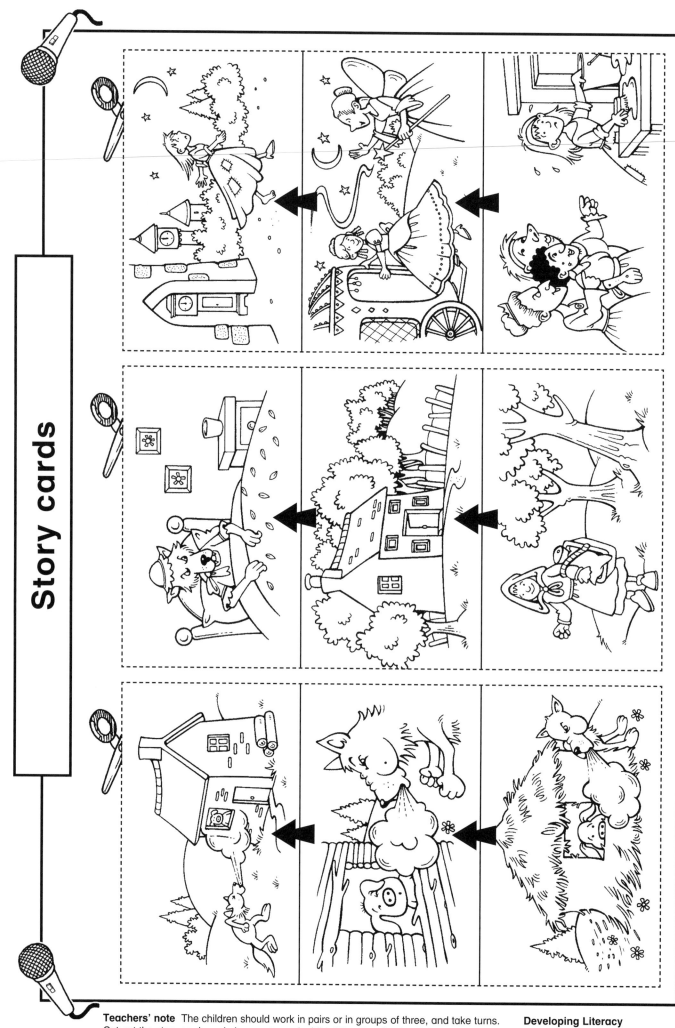

Teachers' note The children should work in pairs or in groups of three, and take turns. Cut out the story cards and give one to each child. Allow time for the children to look at the cards and recognise the story. Ask them to name the characters and describe the setting, before telling the part of the story shown. They can then continue the stories to the end.

Developing Literacy
Speaking & Listening
Year 1
© A & C BLACK

16

The Gingerbread Man

- **Read the story to yourself.**
- **Which words are** LOUD ?

  Colour these words red .

The Gingerbread Man

A little old woman made a gingerbread man.
She put him in the oven.

"Let me out! Let me out!" came from the oven.

"No!" she called. "I'm going to eat you."

The little old woman got on with her work.

"The gingerbread man will be cooked now," she said.

She opened the oven. Out jumped the gingerbread man.
He ran out of the door.

"Run, run as fast as you can! You can't catch me,
I'm the gingerbread man!" he sang, as he ran down
the path.

"Come back! I want to eat you,"
cried the little old woman,
and she ran after him.

- **Read the story to a friend.**
- **Tell the rest of the story.**

Teachers' note Tell the children the story of *The Gingerbread Man*. Then read the passage, emphasising the loud and quiet parts of the story. Read the passage again, this time without any change of tone. Discuss which sounds better, and why. Some children might need to read the story with an adult or with a good reader in order to identify the words which should be read loudly.

Developing Literacy
Speaking & Listening
Year 1
© A & C BLACK

Say the words

What are they saying?

- **Say the words.**

- **Write the words.**

Work with a friend.

Now try this!

- **Draw a picture about a bike.**

- **Say the words.** Work with a friend.

Teachers' note Give each child a copy of the page and ask them about the setting and characters in this story. What is happening in each picture? Encourage the children to say what the characters are doing; then point out the blank speech bubbles and ask them to think about what the characters might be saying, and to whom. How can they tell? Why might the character say this?

Developing Literacy
Speaking & Listening
Year 1
© A & C BLACK

- **Listen to a story.**

- **Draw 2 of the** characters **.**

- **Write words that describe them.**

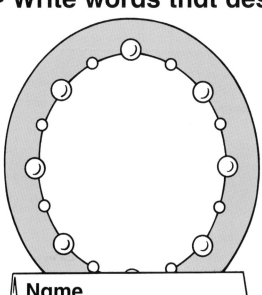

Name

_____

_____

_____

_____

_____

Name

_____

_____

_____

_____

- **Choose a character from another story.**

- **Tell a friend about the character.**

Teachers' note Choose a story to read to the class. Before you read it, ensure that the children know what is meant by 'a character', and point out that a character can be human or an animal. When completing the activity, the children could work individually, in pairs or in groups of three or four. For group work, the page could be enlarged to A3 and an adult could act as scribe.

Developing Literacy
Speaking & Listening
Year 1
© A & C BLACK

The Big Pancake

- **Where did the pancake go?**

Write the words.

Word bank

gate

wall

door

field

path

out of the _____

along the _____

and out of the _____

It passed a man in a _____

and a cat on a _____

- **What did the pancake pass next?**

Draw and label 2 people or animals.

Teachers' note Read *The Big Pancake* (Ladybird) with the children and invite them to name the people and animals the pancake passed. Enlarge the page to A3 if necessary. After completing the story map, the children could retell the story up to this point, using the map as a prompt. You could help them to continue the story map on another piece of paper. (If necessary, re-read the story.)

Developing Literacy Speaking & Listening Year 1 © A & C BLACK

Spike the hungry hedgehog

• **What did Spike eat?**

Write the numbers and words.

Word bank

slug   ants   worms

beetles   spiders

Monday	I	_____
Tuesday		_____
Wednesday		_____
Thursday		_____
Friday		_____

• **Draw 6 things Spike ate on** Saturday .

Teachers' note Make up a story about Spike the hungry hedgehog, where he eats one slug on Monday, two worms on Tuesday, three beetles on Wednesday, and so on (refer to the pictures in the word bank). Ask the children to notice what Spike eats each day, and how many. When you have finished telling the story, ask the children to try to remember what Spike ate.

**Developing Literacy
Speaking & Listening
Year 1
© A & C BLACK**

The sunflower

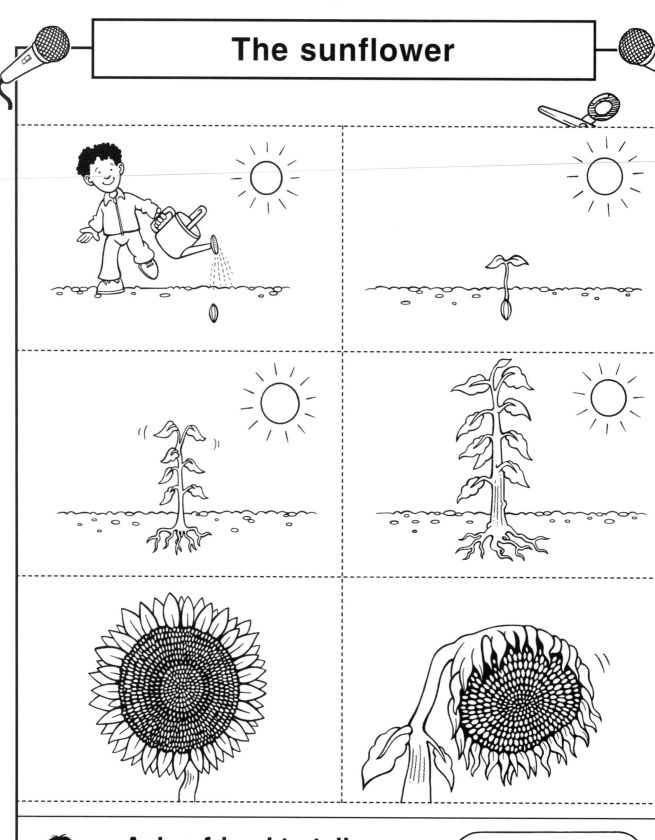

- **Ask a friend to tell you about another life cycle.**
- **Draw pictures of it. Write labels.**

It could be a plant or an animal.

Teachers' note The children should work in pairs. Give one of them a copy of the page intact and the other a copy from which the pictures have been cut out and mixed up. The child who has the intact page tells the other what the series of pictures is about and then what is happening in each picture. The other child listens and puts the pictures in order.

Developing Literacy Speaking & Listening Year 1 © A & C BLACK

Pattern cards

Don't let your friend see the pattern.

Use different colours and shapes.

- Take it in turns to look at a pattern.
- Tell a friend how to make it.

- Make a model from 4 shapes.
- Tell a friend how to make it.

Now try this!

Teachers' note The children should work in pairs. Cut out the cards and give two, face down, to each partner. The children take turns to describe a pattern for their partner to make using 2-D shapes. Encourage the child who is listening to ask for help or clarification if necessary.

Developing Literacy
Speaking & Listening
Year 1
© A & C BLACK

Pirate treasure

- **Choose a place to hide the treasure.**
- **Tell a friend how to find it.**

Don't say the name of the place!

Wild Woods

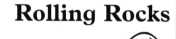
Rolling Rocks

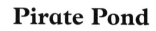
Pirate Pond

old well

**fir
tree**

cottage

tower

Creepy Cave

apple tree

old
boat

Start here

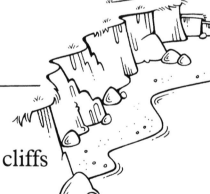

cliffs

sea

- **Choose something in the classroom.**
- **Tell a friend how to find it.**

Teachers' note The children should work in pairs, taking turns to 'hide' and 'find' the treasure. Both children will need a copy of the sheet. They might first need practice in using words for directions: for example, *along, left, right, stop, straight on, turn*. Encourage them to use landmarks such as the tower and the cliffs in their directions. The child following the instructions may ask for help and clarification.

**Developing Literacy
Speaking & Listening
Year 1**
© A & C BLACK

24

Make a minibeast

Your friend is going to make this snail.

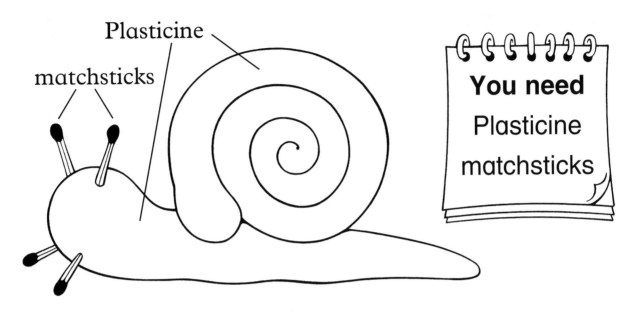

Plasticine

matchsticks

You need

Plasticine

matchsticks

- **Tell your friend what they need.**

- **Tell them what to do.**

Your friend is going to make this spider.

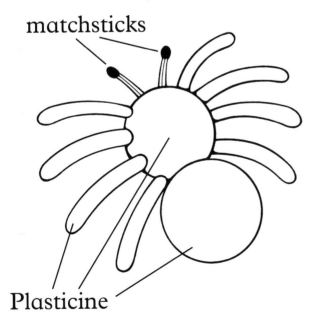

matchsticks

Plasticine

You need

Plasticine

matchsticks

- **Tell your friend what they need.**

- **Tell them what to do.**

Teachers' note The children should work in pairs. Cut the sheet in half and give one half to each child (each child should keep their picture hidden). Provide Plasticine and spent matchsticks for making the models, and tell the children that they should take turns to give/listen to instructions. The child following the instructions may ask for help and clarification if necessary.

Developing Literacy
Speaking & Listening
Year 1
© A & C BLACK

Story tape

Work with a group.

- **Listen to a story tape.**

  Did you like how it was read?

- **Fill in the chart.**

Title _____

_____

Author _____

Narrator _____

What we thought of   😊 ☹ 😐

the narrator's voice	🙂	the characters' voices	🙂
the music	🙂	the other sounds	🙂

Now try this!

- **Make your own story tape.**

- **Change your voice for each character.**

Choose a story you know well.

Teachers' note This page can be used with any story tape/CD. The children should have read the book before they listen to the recording. Introduce or revise the following terms: *title, cover, author, narrator, characters.* Play the tape and discuss how it is similar to/different from the book. The children should fill in the chart as a group. They will need tape recorders for the extension activity.

Developing Literacy
Speaking & Listening
Year 1
© A & C BLACK

Information video

Work with a group.

ALL ABOUT CATS

- ## Watch an information video.
- ## Fill in the chart.

The video was about _____	

The video had ✔

real-life pictures ☐

cartoons ☐

diagrams ☐

music ☐

talking ☐

We liked 🙂	We did not like 🙁
_____	_____
_____	_____
_____	_____
_____	_____

Now try this!

- ## What did you learn from the video?
Write a list.

Teachers' note This page can be used with any information video/DVD on a topic the children are learning about in another subject. Play the video, then ask the children what they liked best about the video, and why. Did it help them to learn about the topic? Did it make it more interesting? The children should fill in the chart as a group, led by an adult if necessary.

**Developing Literacy
Speaking & Listening
Year 1
© A & C BLACK**

Story video

- **Watch a story video.**

- **Draw one of the characters.**

- **Write about the character.**

Name

_____

Human or animal

_____

Boy or girl

_____

Good or bad _____

How I know _____

_____

_____

_____

_____

_____

- **What would you like to do if you met this character? Talk to a friend.**

Teachers' note This page can be used with any fiction video/DVD. Begin by showing the children the cover and introducing or revising the following terms: *title, cover, author, narrator, characters*. Discuss how the video is similar to/different from a book or a story tape (see page 7). During the plenary, discuss what the children enjoyed about watching the video.

Developing Literacy Speaking & Listening Year 1 © A & C BLACK

Rhyme characters

- **Work with a group.**
- **Take turns to pick a character.**
- **Answer the group's questions about your character.**

Don't tell your group who it is.

Georgie Porgie

The farmer's wife

Mary

Old Mother Hubbard

The Grand Old Duke of York

Tom, the piper's son

- **What might happen if all these characters met?**

Talk to a friend. Write about it.

Teachers' note The children should first have listened to or read and joined in the reciting of the nursery rhymes *Georgie Porgie, Three Blind Mice, Mary Had a Little Lamb, Old Mother Hubbard, The Grand Old Duke of York* and *Tom, Tom, the Piper's Son*. Model how to ask and answer questions about a character (see page 7).

**Developing Literacy
Speaking & Listening
Year 1
© A & C BLACK**

Animal partners

cat

owl

snail

goldfish

chimpanzee

sheep

spider

lizard

ladybird

duck

crab

worm

Teachers' note Make two copies of this page for a group of up to 24 children. Give each child an animal card, ensuring that another child also has the same animal. Tell the children not to let anyone else see their cards. Explain that they have to find their 'partner', i.e. the other child who has the same animal, by asking questions which can be answered by 'Yes' or 'No' (see page 7).

Developing Literacy
Speaking & Listening
Year 1
© A & C BLACK

30

Rules

☆ 4 can play.

☆ Each player puts a counter on START.

☆ The first to FINISH wins.

Work with a group.

How can you make the game fair?

• Ask one question each.

Talk about the answer.

How do you know how far to move your counter?	Who moves first?
How will all players have the same number of turns?	Are all the instructions on the board fair?

Now try this!

• Write 3 new rules for the game.

Work with a friend.

Teachers' note Use this with page 32. Invite volunteers to read the rules and encourage the children, in groups of four, to discuss what else they need to decide before they play the game, such as whether to use a dice or spinner. Let the children try playing the game. Do they have any difficulties? Discuss why. Read the questions with them, cut them out and give one to each child. See also page 32.

Developing Literacy Speaking & Listening Year 1 © A & C BLACK

Racer: 2

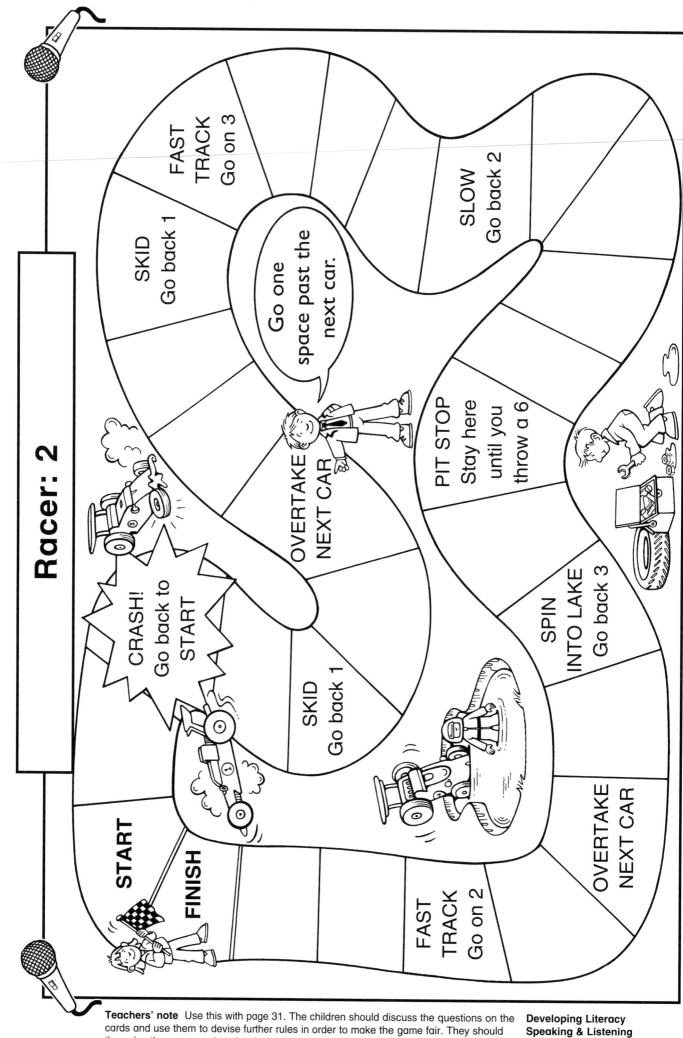

FAST TRACK Go on 3

SKID Go back 1

Go one space past the next car.

SLOW Go back 2

OVERTAKE NEXT CAR

PIT STOP Stay here until you throw a 6

CRASH! Go back to START

SKID Go back 1

SPIN INTO LAKE Go back 3

START

FINISH

FAST TRACK Go on 2

OVERTAKE NEXT CAR

Teachers' note Use this with page 31. The children should discuss the questions on the cards and use them to devise further rules in order to make the game fair. They should then play the game again using their rules (they may make changes if they wish). The children might find it helpful to number the spaces, beginning with START as number 1.

**Developing Literacy
Speaking & Listening
Year 1
© A & C BLACK**

Giving presents

- **Which is the best present for each person?**

  Talk to your group.

Dad **Mum**

Lisa   Callum   Ellie

- **Draw lines to join the presents to the people.**

- **What present would you buy for your teacher?**

  Talk to a friend.

Teachers' note The children should work in small groups. Allow time for them to consider individually which present they would give to each person. Explain that there is no 'right answer'. Each child should tell the group their ideas, giving reasons, and the others should ask questions about their choices. The group should vote for the best present for each person and draw the joining lines.

**Developing Literacy
Speaking & Listening
Year 1
© A & C BLACK**

All kinds of books

• **What kinds of books do you like best?**

or

big books ☐   small books ☐

or

a lot of pictures ☐   a few pictures ☐

information books ☐

or

storybooks ☐   rhymes ☐

• **Talk to your group about what you chose.**

  • **Tell the class about your**

group's likes **and** dislikes .

Teachers' note First let the children look at a collection of books from the class library. Include books of the types shown on this page and encourage the children to identify different kinds of books using these criteria. After considering their preferences individually, the children should form small groups. For the extension activity, they will need to decide how to report their group's opinions to the class.

Developing Literacy
Speaking & Listening
Year 1
© A & C BLACK

Favourite story setting

- **Vote for your favourite** story setting.

Colour one box for each person.

Start at the bottom. Work with a group.

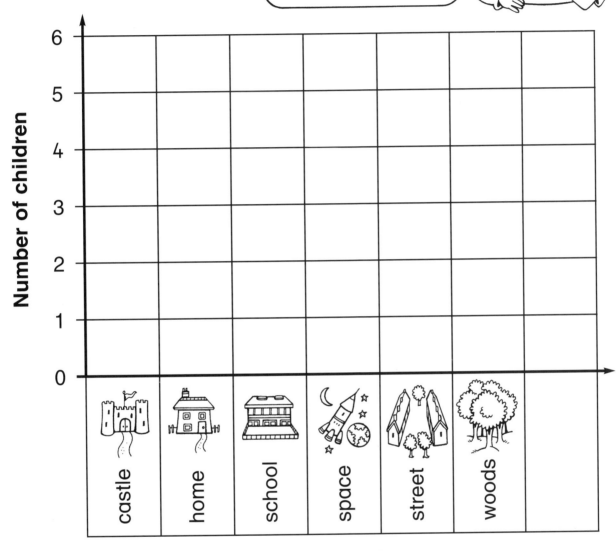

Number of children

6
5
4
3
2
1
0

castle   home   school   space   street   woods

Story setting

- **Which story setting did you choose?**

Tell your group why you like it.

Now try this!

- **Tell the class about your graph.**

Who will do the talking?

Teachers' note The children should work in groups of up to six. Remind them of the meaning of 'story setting' and ask them about the settings of books they have read. Which settings did they like? If any of these are not shown on the graph, they could be substituted for those shown; a blank column is also provided for another setting. During the plenary, discuss which story settings are the most popular.

Developing Literacy Speaking & Listening Year 1 © A & C BLACK

Our classroom

Work with a group.

- ● **Talk about your classroom.**

- ● **Write notes.**

We like

_____

_____

_____

We do not like

_____

_____

_____

Now try this!

- ● **How could you make your classroom better? Talk to your group.**

- ● **Choose one of your ideas. Draw and write about it.**

Teachers' note Ask the children to think about what they like about their classroom. They could begin by telling a partner and then listening to what their partner says. They could present their partner's views to the group. An adult or a child who is good at writing could act as scribe for the group. Once they have talked about what they like, ask the children to share their views about what they dislike.

Developing Literacy Speaking & Listening Year 1 © A & C BLACK

> I don't like wet playtimes. We have to stay indoors.

> It's boring!

• **What could be done to make things better?**

Talk to your group.

Our ideas

Now try this!

• **Choose the best idea.**

Tell the class about it.

> Say why it is a good idea.

Teachers' note The problem could be substituted by one which is relevant to the class. Point out that the children should consider every idea and list/draw them all on the notepad. Encourage the children to explain how their ideas would help to solve the problem. They should vote for their group's best idea and decide how to present it to the class. The class could vote for the best idea overall.

**Developing Literacy
Speaking & Listening
Year 1
© A & C BLACK**

Wolf mask

- **Cut out the mask.**

- **Act a story.**

Teachers' note Photocopy this page onto card and ask the children to colour and cut out the mask. Use a hole puncher to make holes in the shaded circles, then loop an elastic band through each hole. The children should wear the masks (with the elastic loops over their ears) to enact the role of any wolf in a story (see page 8). Using this with page 39, a group can enact *The Wolf and the Seven Little Kids*.

Developing Literacy Speaking & Listening Year 1 © A & C BLACK

Goat mask

- **Cut out the mask.**
- **Act a story.**

Teachers' note Photocopy this page onto card and ask the children to colour and cut out the mask. Use a hole puncher to make holes in the shaded circles, then loop an elastic band through each hole. The children should wear the masks (with the elastic loops over their ears) to enact the role of any goat in a story (see page 8). Using this with page 38, a group can enact *The Wolf and the Seven Little Kids*.

Developing Literacy Speaking & Listening Year 1 © A & C BLACK

39

A magic story

- **Work with a friend.**
- **Act a story.**

  Use magic.

Use different voices.

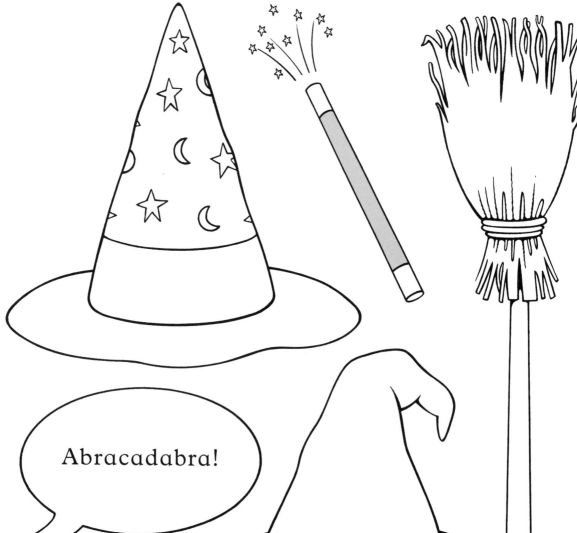

Abracadabra!

Now try this!

- **What happens because of the magic?**

  Act the end of the story.

Teachers' note First ask the children how characters in stories use good/bad magic. Discuss the pictures and how the children might use these items in magic spells. They could make up their own 'magic words' to replace 'Abracadabra'. The main activity explores magic in a story; the conclusion is enacted in the extension activity. Help the children to decide on different voices for each character.

**Developing Literacy
Speaking & Listening
Year 1
© A & C BLACK**

My story character

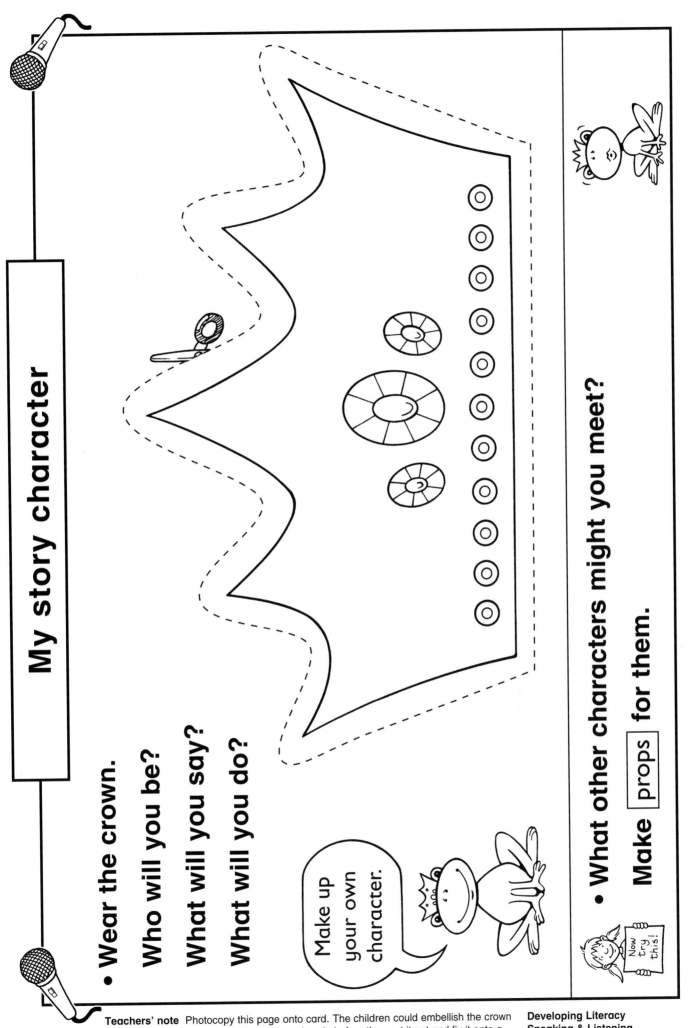

- Wear the crown.

Who will you be?

What will you say?

What will you do?

Make up your own character.

- What other characters might you meet?

Make | props | for them.

Teachers' note Photocopy this page onto card. The children could embellish the crown with gold foil and glue on plastic beads as jewels before they cut it out and fix it onto a pre-prepared card headband. The children wear the crown as they enact the role of their character. Ask them if their character is good or bad and how they will show this.

**Developing Literacy
Speaking & Listening
Year 1
© A & C BLACK**

Cinderella

Cinderella's sisters bullied her. What if her friends came to help? What could they say?

- **Work with a group.**

- **Act the scene.**

- **Act the story to the end.**

Teachers' note The children should work in groups of four (with one friend arriving to help) or five (with two friends arriving). Encourage them to use their voices to express the characters' feelings. They could swap roles; this gives them an opportunity to explore how what a character does and says can affect the outcome, and encourages them to use different voices.

**Developing Literacy
Speaking & Listening
Year 1
© A & C BLACK**

42

Goldilocks in the hot seat

- **What would you like to ask Goldilocks?**

- **Imagine a police officer talks to Goldilocks.**
- Role-play **the questions and answers.**

Now try this!

Work with a friend.

Teachers' note This page is designed to help the children prepare for a 'hot seat' activity in which one child takes the role of Goldilocks and answers questions in role. Preparing in this way helps the children to ask more imaginative questions than they would with no preparation. The children could work in pairs to think of questions.

**Developing Literacy
Speaking & Listening
Year 1
© A & C BLACK**

The Sleeping Beauty

- **Be a good fairy.**

  Write your wish for the baby.

  I wish _____

  _____

  _____

  _____

- **Work with a group.**

  Act the scene.

  Now try this!

- **Imagine your good wish came true.**

  Act the story with a friend.

Teachers' note The children should first have read *The Sleeping Beauty*. Help them to retell the story, and discuss the effects of the magic spells cast by the good fairies and bad fairy as they made wishes for the baby. Focus on the wishes themselves; draw out that the fairies did not wish for objects but made wishes for the baby's character and for events in her life.

Developing Literacy
Speaking & Listening
Year 1
© A & C BLACK

Who's talking?

- **Work with a friend.**

- **Take turns to read the story aloud.**

- **What did your friend like about the way you read the story?**

- **Tell the whole story from the pictures. Record it.**

Teachers' note This is based on *The Great Big Enormous Turnip* (Alexei Tolstoy, Ladybird). Read the opening of the story from the book, up to the point where the man goes out to pull up the turnip (or make up the story opening). Model how to use your voice expressively to show when a new character is speaking. The children will need tape recorders for the extension activity.

**Developing Literacy
Speaking & Listening
Year 1**
© A & C BLACK

The Emperor's New Clothes

- **Work in a group of 6.**
- **Mime this scene.**

One of you should watch.

Don't dress up or undress!

The tailors   **The emperor**   **His ministers**

- **Could the person watching tell who these characters were?** ✔ **or** ✘

The emperor ☐   His ministers ☐

The tailors ☐

- **How could they tell? Talk to your group.**

Now try this!

- **Work in a group of 4.**
- **Mime the scene where the emperor puts on the clothes.**

One of you should watch.

Teachers' note Tell the story of *The Emperor's New Clothes*, up to the point where the tailors present the new clothes to the emperor. Draw out that the tailors have tricked the emperor, and discuss why he and his ministers pretend that they can see the clothes. Then discuss what each character in the picture is doing and how they feel. Explain that miming uses no words, only gestures and movement.

Developing Literacy Speaking & Listening Year 1 © A & C BLACK

Jack and the Beanstalk

- **Work with a friend.**

- **Do the actions.**

  Your friend says the words.

- ## How did you use your face, arms, legs and body?

- ## How did you use your voice?

Teachers' note Ask the children to read this picture story (loosely based on *Jack and the Beanstalk*) with a partner – one speaking and the other doing the actions. They should then swap roles. Help them to use their voice, movement and gesture to express the feelings of each character. In the extension activity the children should discuss their own and their partner's performances.

**Developing Literacy
Speaking & Listening
Year 1
© A & C BLACK**

How did you do?

My name _____

Name of activity _____

_____

• Colour a face.

I spoke clearly.

I remembered to look up.

I listened carefully.

I asked questions.

What? Where? When? Why?

When I talked with my friends, I took turns.

Teachers' note Photocopy this page and fill in the title of the activity to be self-assessed. Before the children complete the assessment sheet, ask them whether they enjoyed the activity, and why or why not. Read through the questions and, if necessary, help the children to complete the sheet.

**Developing Literacy
Speaking & Listening
Year 1**
© A & C BLACK